Great Songwriters

15 great songs arranged for Easy Piano by **Dan Coates**

Published 2002

Editor Chris Harvey
Design IMP Studio

Music Arrangements Dan Coates
Cover Image George & Ira Gershwin © 2002 Michael Ochs Archive / Redferns Music Picture Library

Photo by Carin A. Baer

Dan Coates

As a student at the University of Miami, Dan Coates paid his tuition by playing the piano at south Florida nightclubs and restaurants. One evening in 1975, after Dan had worked his unique brand of magic on the ivories, a stranger from the music field walked up and told him that he should put his inspired piano arrangements down on paper so they could be published.

Dan took the stranger's advice—and the world of music has become much richer as a result. Since that chance encounter long ago, Dan has gone on to achieve international acclaim for his brilliant piano arrangements. His Big Note, Easy Piano and Professional Touch arrangements have inspired countless piano students and established themselves as classics against which all other works must be measured.

Enjoying an exclusive association with Warner Bros. Publications since 1982, Dan has demonstrated a unique gift for writing arrangements intended for students of every level, from beginner to advanced. Dan never fails to bring a fresh and original approach to his work. Pushing his own creative boundaries with each new manuscript, he writes material that is musically exciting and educationally sound.

From the very beginning of his musical life, Dan has always been eager to seek new challenges. As a five-year-old in Syracuse, New York, he used to sneak into the home of his neighbours to play their piano. Blessed with an amazing ear for music, Dan was able to imitate the melodies of songs he had heard on the radio. Finally, his neighbours convinced his parents to buy Dan his own piano. At that point, there was no stopping his musical development. Dan won a prestigious New York State competition for music composers at the age of 15. Then, after graduating from high school, he toured the world as an arranger and pianist with the group Up With People.

Later, Dan studied piano at the University of Miami with the legendary Ivan Davis, developing his natural abilities to stylize music on the keyboard. Continuing to perform professionally during and after his college years, Dan has played the piano on national television and at the 1984 Summer Olympics in Los Angeles. He has also accompanied recording artists as diverse as Dusty Springfield and Charlotte Rae.

During his long and prolific association with Warner Bros. Publications, Dan has written many award-winning books. He conducts piano workshops worldwide, demonstrating his famous arrangements with a special spark that never fails to inspire students and teachers alike.

As Time Goes By

Words and Music by Herman Hupfeld

C A7 Dm7 G7
And when two lov - ers woo, they
Gm G7 C Dm7
still say, "I love you," on that you can re - ly;
D♯dim7 C/E Am7 D7
no mat - ter what the fu - ture
Dm7 G7 C F Fm C C7
brings, as time goes by.
F A7
Moon - light and love songs nev - er out of date,
mf

Dm D♯dim Am F7
hearts full of pas-sion, jeal-ous-y and hate; wo-man needs man and
D7 G7 C♯dim7 Dm7 G7
man must have his mate; that no one can de - ny. It's
Dm7 G7 Gm G7
still the same old sto-ry, a fight for love and glo-ry, a
mp
C Dm7 D♯dim7 C/E Am7 D7
case of do or die! The world will al - ways wel - come
(cresc.)
mf
C A7 Dm7 G G+ 1. C A7 2. C
lov - ers, as time goes by. You by.
mp
p

Cabaret

Words by Fred Ebb
Music by John Kander

Dm
F+
Dm7
G7
C7
Come blow the horn, start cel - e - brat - ing right this way, your
F
C7
F
ta - bles wait - ing. No use per - mit - ing some pro - phet of doom
C7
F
F/E
Cm7
F7
to wipe ev - 'ry smile a - way.
B♭
Bdim
Am7
D7
f
Life is a Cab - a - ret, old chum,
Gm7
B♭/C
F
8va
come to the Cab - a - ret.
sfz

Bewitched

Words by Lorenz Hart
Music by Richard Rodgers

C E7 F A♭dim C/G F♯dim
love came and told me I should - n't sleep, Be - witched, both-ered and be -
G7 C7 Fmaj7 A7
wil - dered am I.
Dm Am
Lost my heart, but what of it? He is cold, I a -
mf
Dm7 G7 Dm7 G7
gree. He can laugh, but I love it, al - though the

Em7 F♯dim Dm7 G7 C
laugh's on me. I'll sing to him, each
mp
Dm7 C/G E7 F A♭dim
spring to him, and long for the day when I'll cling to him, Be -
C/G F♯dim Dm7 G7 1.C Am
witched, both-ered and be - wil - dered am I.
mp
Dm7 G7 G7+5 2. C Fm6 C
I'm I.
rit.
p

High Hopes

Words by Sammy Cahn
Music by Jimmy Van Heusen

Gm G#dim Gm7 C7 F
ant can't move a rub-ber tree plant. But he's got
ram scram, he kept but-tin' that dam. 'Cause he had
3. So keep your
Bb Bdim F
high hopes, he's got high
high hopes, he had high
high hopes, keep your high
Dm7 G7
hopes; he's got high ap - ple pie in the
hopes; he had high ap - ple pie in the
hopes; keep those high ap - ple pie in the
C F
sky hopes. So an - y time you're get - tin' low,
sky hopes. So an - y time you're feel - in' bad,
sky hopes. A prob-lem's just a toy bal-loon,

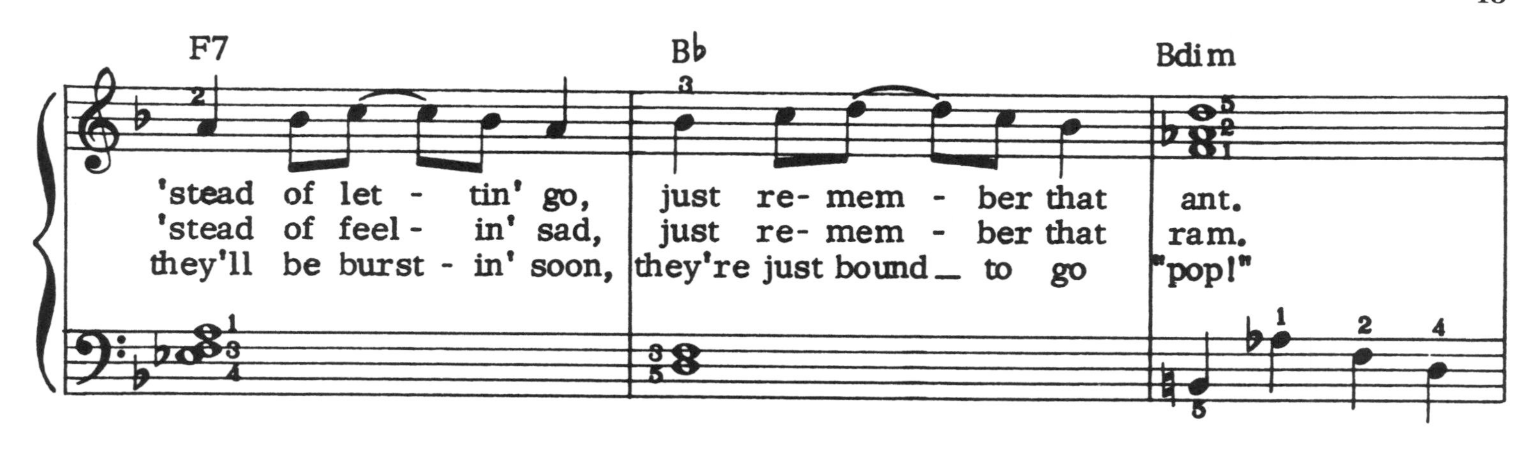
F7
Bb
Bdim
'stead of let - tin' go, just re- mem - ber that ant.
'stead of feel - in' sad, just re- mem - ber that ram.
they'll be burst - in' soon, they're just bound _ to go "pop!"

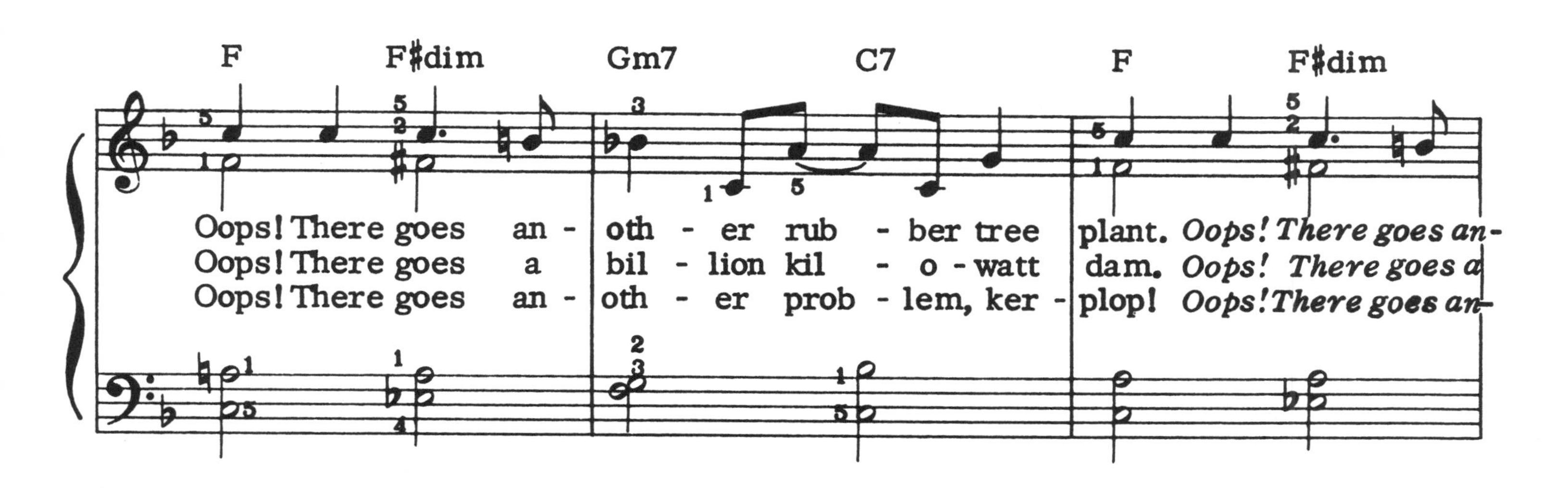
F
F#dim
Gm7
C7
F
F#dim
Oops! There goes an - oth - er rub - ber tree plant. Oops! There goes an-
Oops! There goes a bil - lion kil - o - watt dam. Oops! There goes a
Oops! There goes an - oth - er prob - lem, ker - plop! Oops! There goes an-

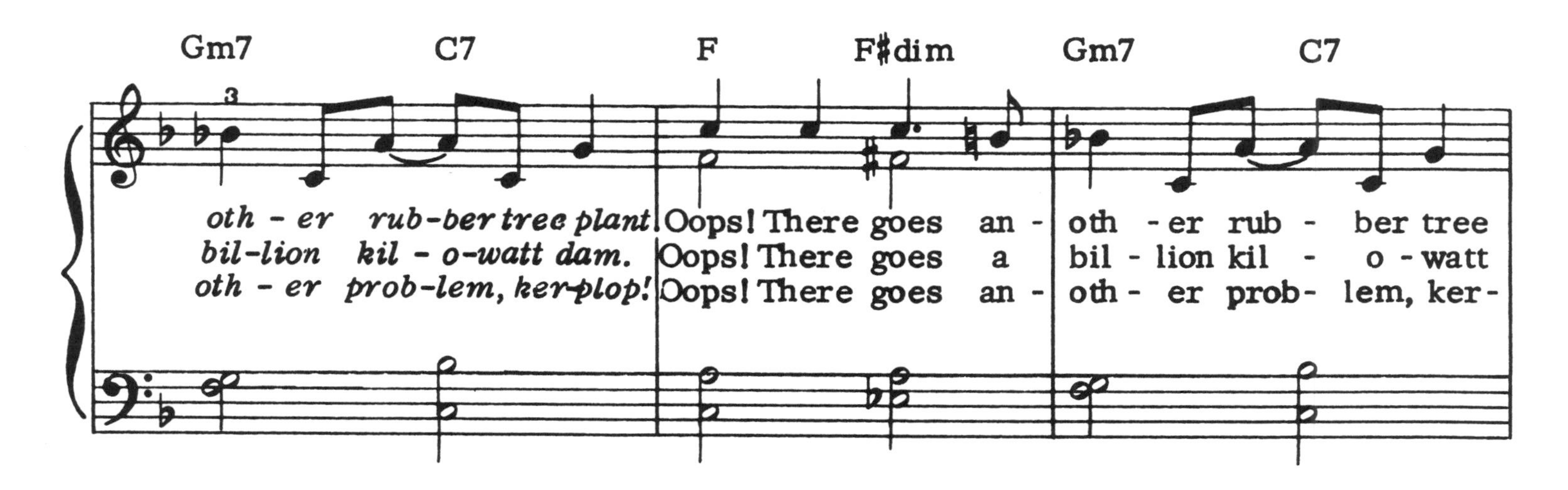
Gm7
C7
F
F#dim
Gm7
C7
oth - er rub-ber tree plant. Oops! There goes an - oth - er rub - ber tree
bil-lion kil - o-watt dam. Oops! There goes a bil - lion kil - o - watt
oth - er prob-lem, ker-plop! Oops! There goes an - oth - er prob- lem, ker-

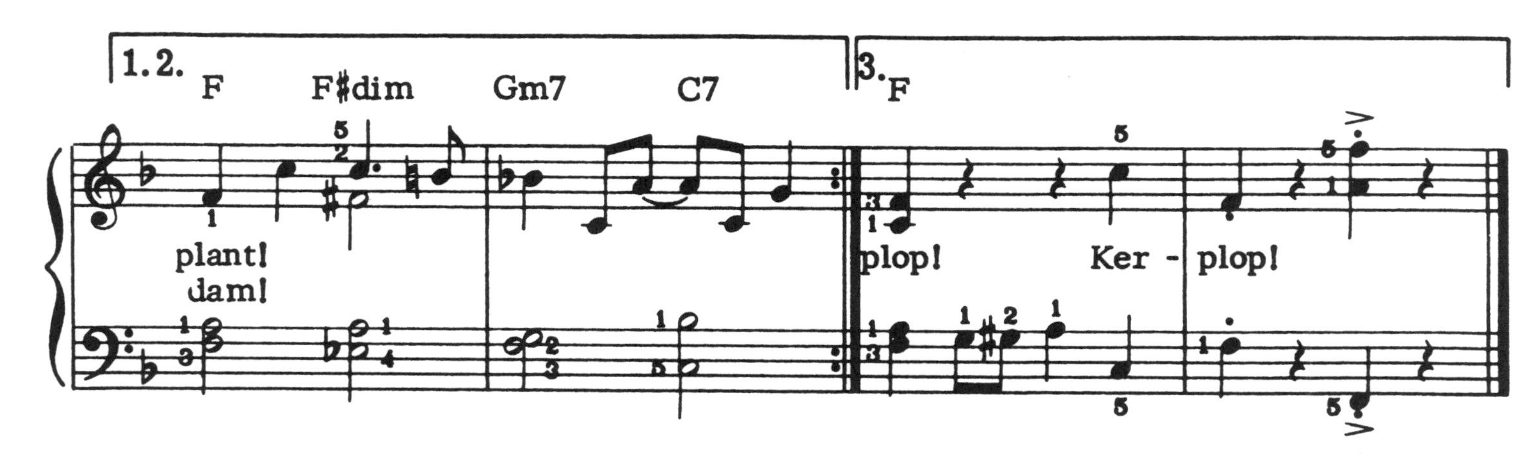
1.2.
F
F#dim
Gm7
C7
3.
F
plant!
dam!
plop! Ker - plop!

I Got Plenty O' Nuttin'

Music and Lyrics by George Gershwin, Du Bose Heyward,
Dorothy Heyward and Ira Gershwin

E
A
E
C♯
D7
got no mis - er - y.
got the deep blue sea.
The
The
G
Am7
Bm
Am
folks with plen - ty o' plen - ty
folks with plen - ty o' plen - ty
mf
G
Am7
G
B7
got a lock on the door,
got to pray all the day.
E
A
E
A
'fraid some - bod - y's a - go - in' to rob 'em while they's
Seems with plen - ty you sure got to wor - ry how to

E A E C♯ D7
out a - mak - in' more. What
keep the devil a - way, a -
G
for?
way.
Bm Bm7 G♯m7(♭5) Em/B
I got no lock on the door, that's no way to
I ain't a - fret - tin' 'bout hell 'til the time ar -
mp
Bm Bm7 G♯m7 (♭5) Em/B
be. They can steal the
rive. Nev - er wor - ry

Bm
Bm7
G♯m7(♭5)
Em/B
rug from the floor, that's O. K. with
long as I'm well, nev - er one to
Bm
Am7
D
Am7
me, 'cause the things that I prize, like the stars in the
strive to be good, to be bad, what the hell? I is
cresc.
D
Am7
D7
skies, all are free.
glad I's a - live.
G
Am7
Bm
Am7
I got plen - ty o' nut - tin', and
f
mp

G Am7 G B7
nut - tin's plen - ty for me. I
E A E A
got my gal, got my song, got
E A E C♯ D7
heav - en the whole day long. Got my
G C/G G Dm7
gal, got my
mf

G
C/G
G
C
Lord,
got
my
1.
G
song.
(R.H.)
Oh,
2.
G
C
G/B
Am7
song!
G
Dm7
G
p
ff

It Ain't Necessarily So

Music and Lyrics by George Gershwin, Du Bose Heyward,
Dorothy Heyward and Ira Gershwin

2.4
Very lively
Gm
E♭7
A♭
my!
Wa - doo,
(wa - doo,)
Zim-bam bod-dle-oo,
mf
D7
(zim - bam bod-dle - oo,)
Hoo-dle ah da wa da,
(hoo - dle ah da wa da,)
Gm
To Coda
D
D.S. al Coda
a tempo I
Scat - ty wah.
(Scat - ty wah.)
Yeah!
3. Oh,
rit.
Coda
D
Gm
C7
Gm
C7
a tempo I
Yeah! It
ain't ne - ces - sa - ri - ly
so,
it
rit.

Gm C7 Gm C7 Db7
ain't ne - ces - sa - ri - ly so. They tell all you chil - lun the
mf
C7 Db7 A7 D7 Gm
dev - il's a vil - lian, but t'ain't ne - ces - sa - ri - ly so. To
mp
Eb7 Ab D7sus D7
get in - to hea - ven, don't snap for a sev - en! Live clean! Don't have no
G6 C7 F
fault. Oh, I takes that gos - pel when - ev - er it's pos'-ble, but
mf

A7sus A7 D7+ Gm C7
with a grain of salt. Me - thus'-lah lived nine hun-dred
mp
Gm C7 Gm C7 Gm
years, Me - thus'-lah lived nine hun - dred years, but
C7 Db7 C7 Db7 A7 D7
who calls that liv - in' when no gal - 'll give in to no man what's nine hun-dred
mf
Gm Eb7 Am7(b5)
years? I'm preach-in' this ser - mon to
mp

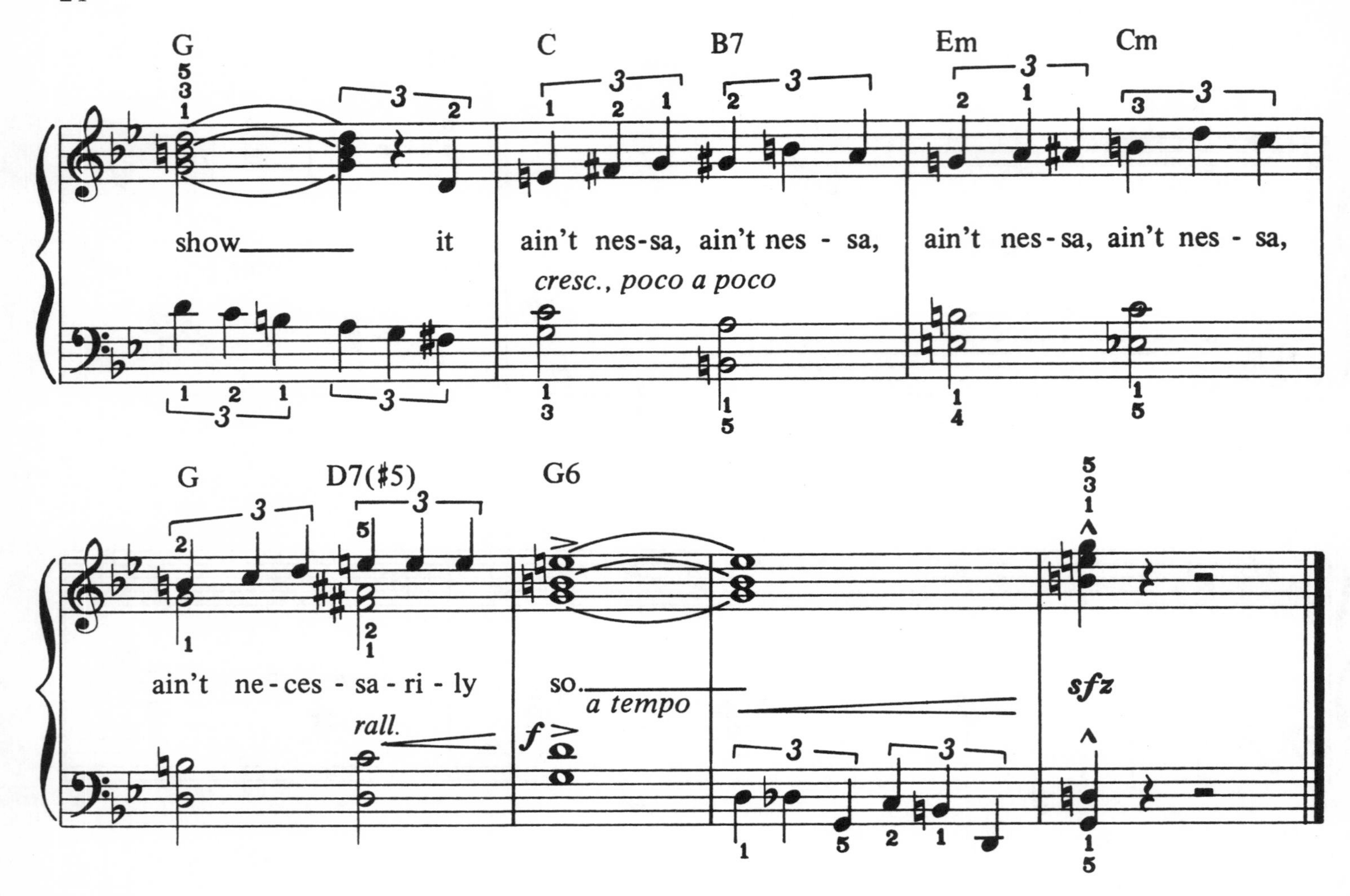

Extra Lyrics:

3.) Oh, Jonah, he lived in the whale,
Oh, Jonah, he lived in the whale,
For he made his home in
That fish's abdomen.
Oh, Jonah, he lived in the whale.

4.) Li'l Moses was found in a stream,
Li'l Moses was found in a stream,
He floated in water
Till Ole Pharaoh's daughter
She fished him, she says, from that stream.

Love And Marriage

Words by Sammy Cahn
Music by Jimmy Van Heusen

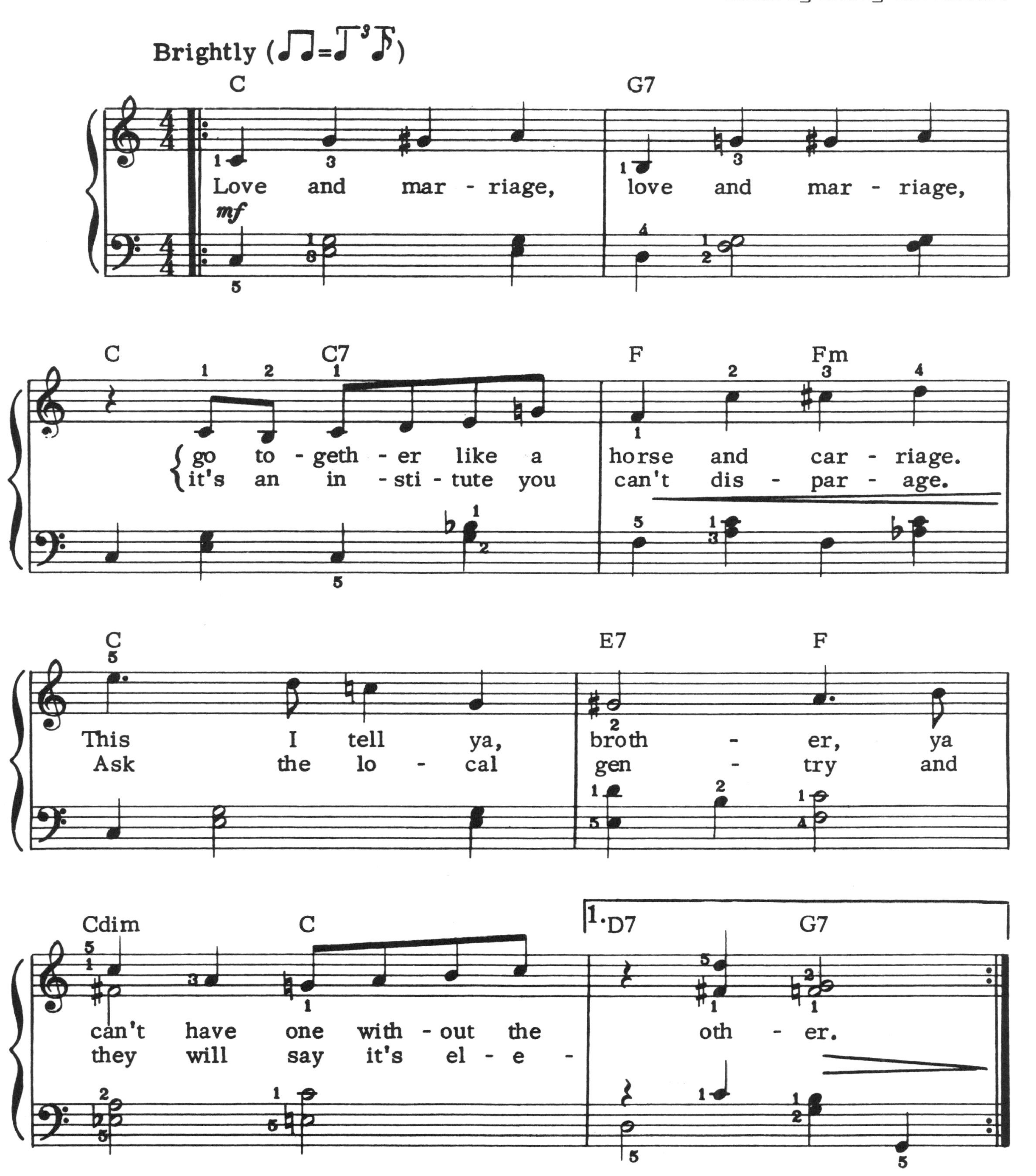

2.
G7 C Ab Abmaj7 Ab6
men - t'ry. Try, try, try to sep - ar - ate them,
mf
Bbm7 Eb7 Ab Abmaj7
it's an il - lu - sion; try, try,
Ab6 C
try and you will on - ly come
G C G7
to this con-clu - sion. Love and mar - riage, love and mar - riage,
mf

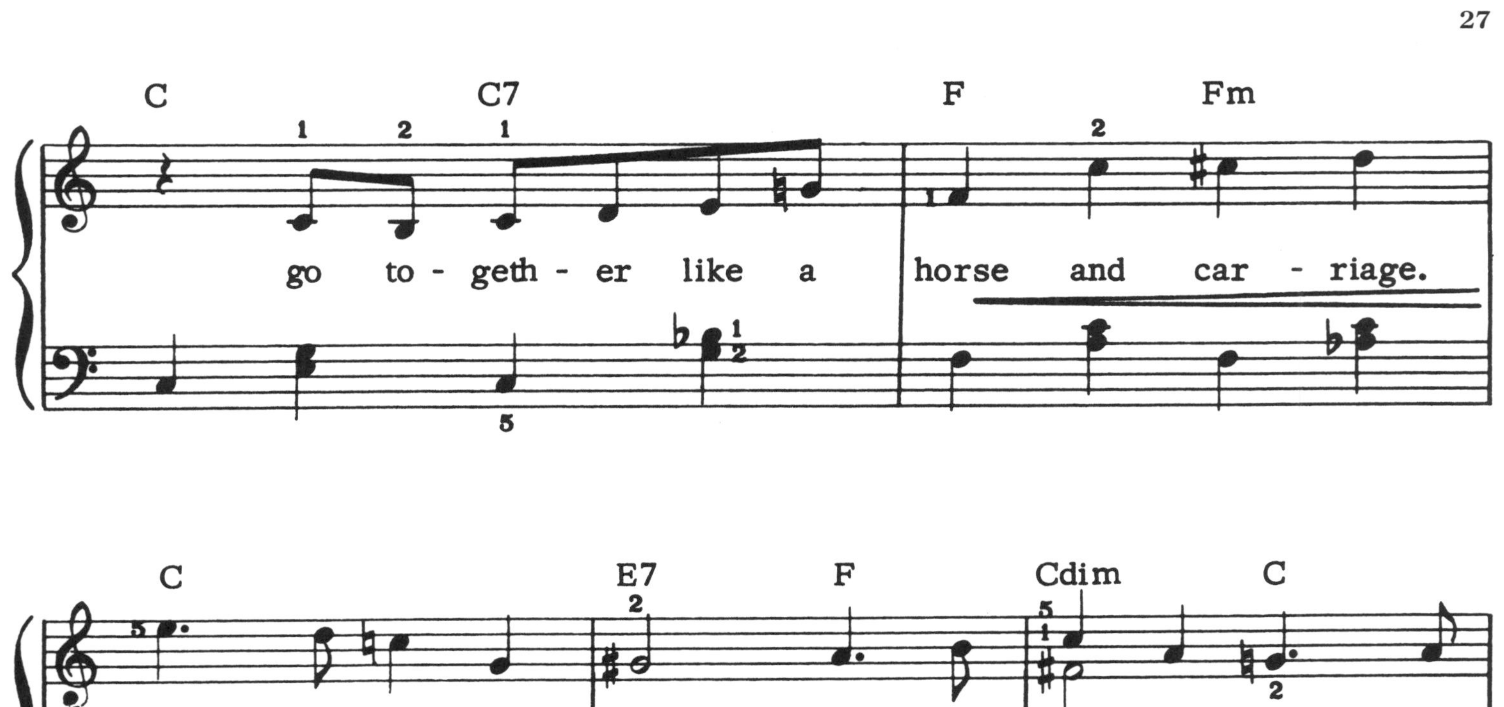
C
C7
F
Fm
go to - geth - er like a horse and car - riage.

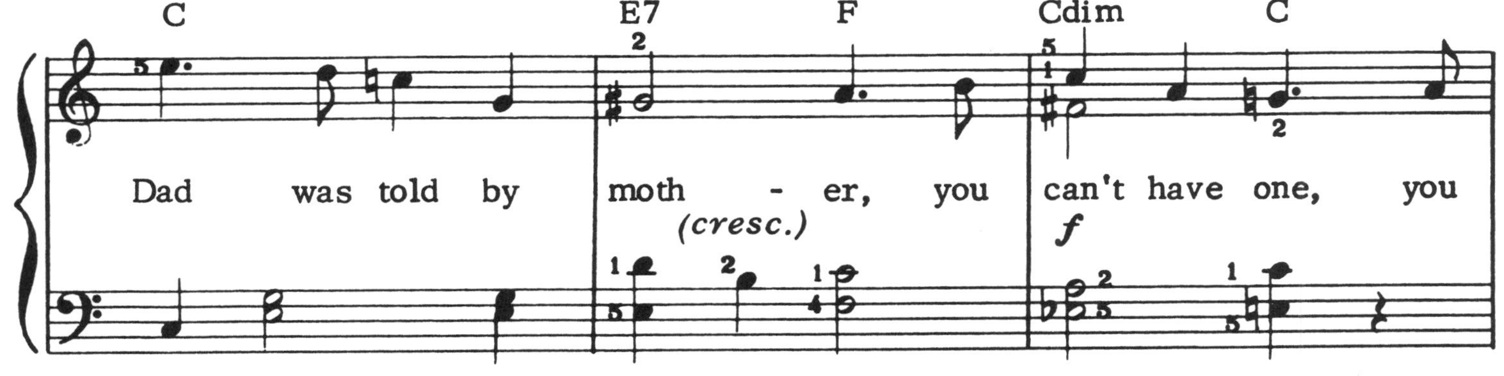
C
E7
F
Cdim
C
Dad was told by moth - er, you can't have one, you
(cresc.)
f

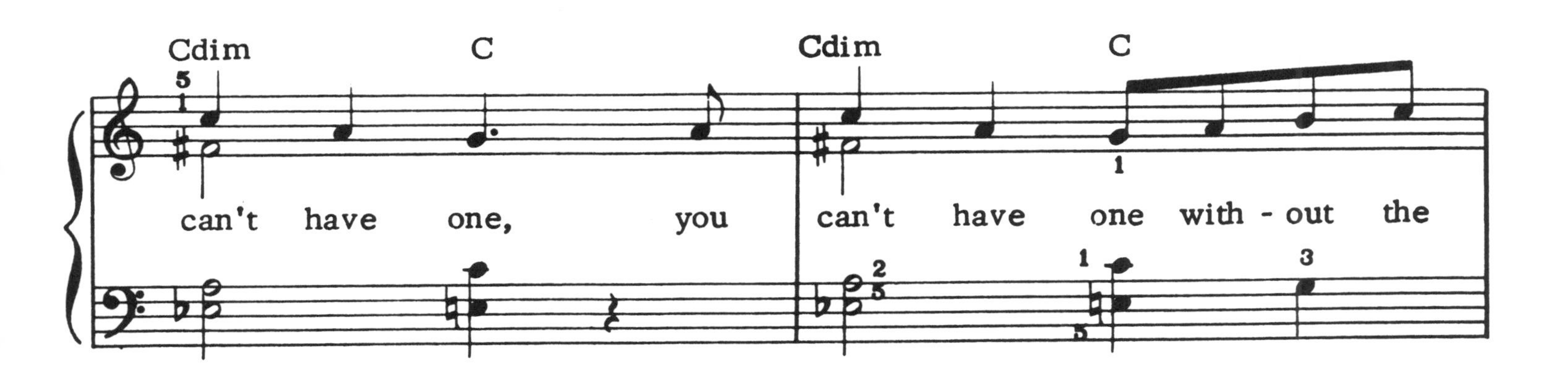
Cdim
C
Cdim
C
can't have one, you can't have one with - out the

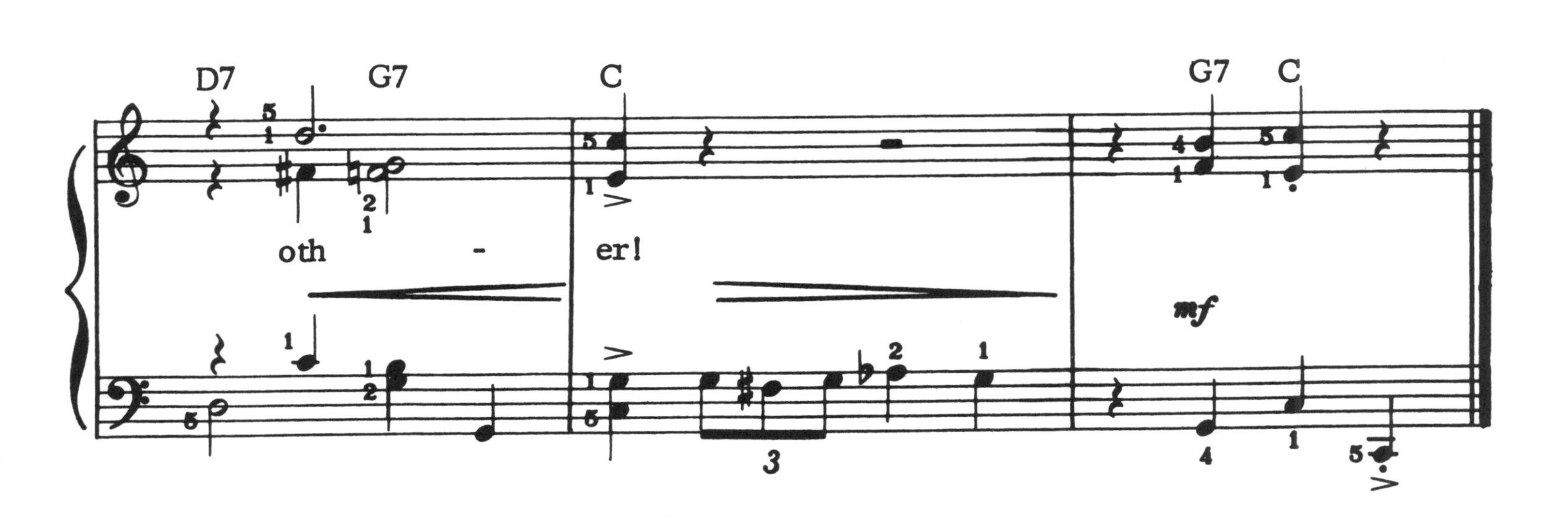
D7
G7
C
G7
C
oth - er!
mf

Maybe This Time

Words by Fred Ebb
Music by John Kander

G7
Cmaj7
C7
F/C
Fm/C
Not a los - er any - more, like the
Coda
C Bb6
A7
Dm
G7
D.C. al Coda
last time and the time be-fore.
G7
mf All the odds are
G7(#5)
Am
Am7
D7/F#
in my fa - vor. Some - thing's bound to be - gin.
Fm6
C/G
C+/G
f It's got to hap - pen, hap-pen some-time.
Am7/G
Dm7
G7
cresc. May - be this time. May - be this time I'll win.
ff
rit

Never Met A Man I Didn't Like

Words by Betty Comden and Adolph Green
Music by Cy Coleman

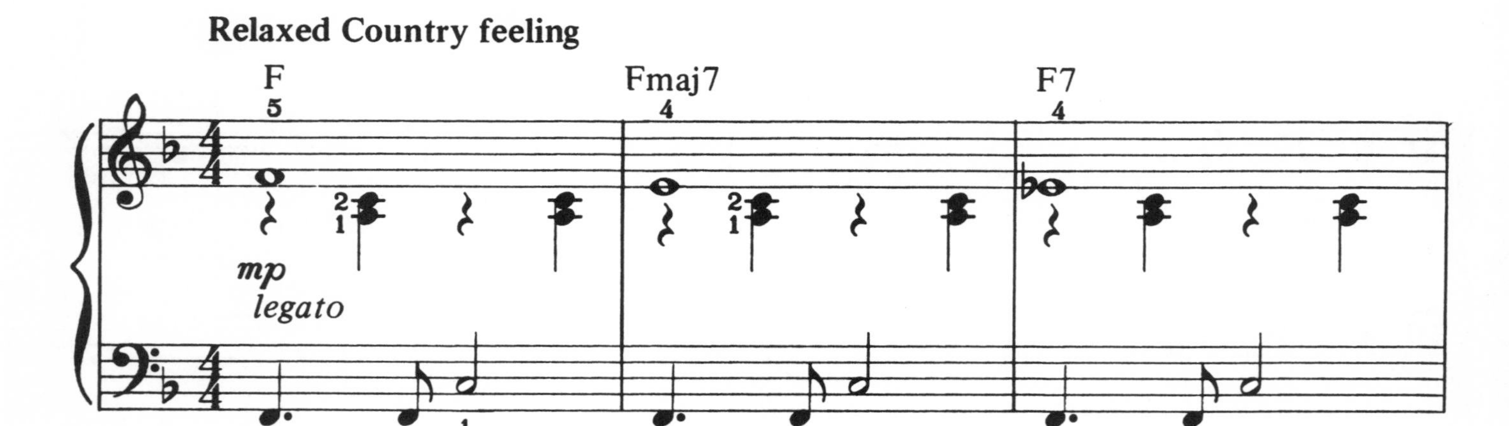

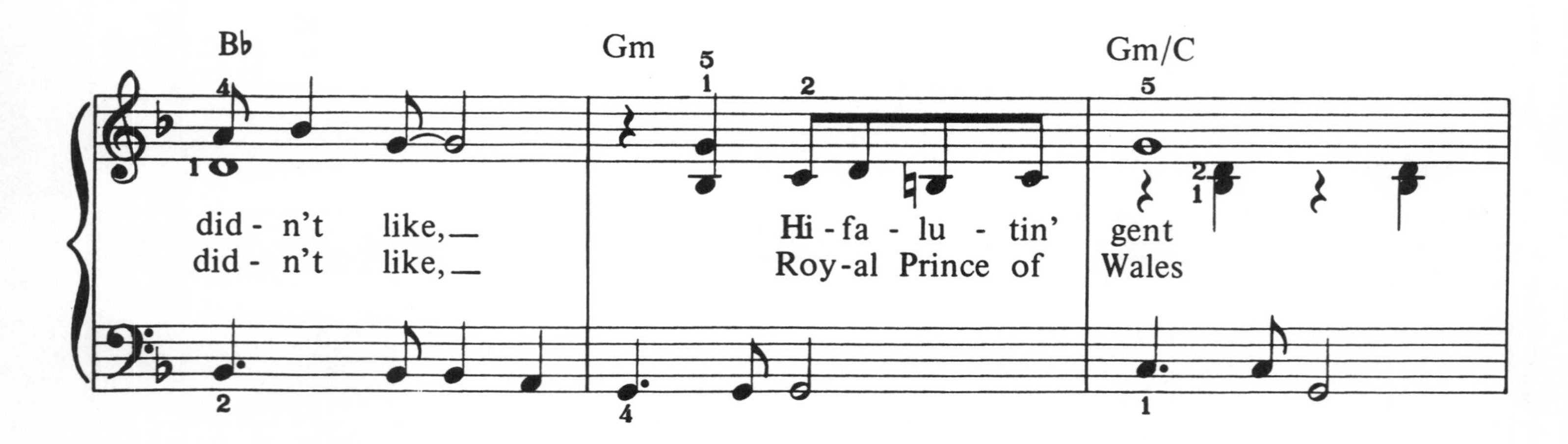

C7
F
Em7
A7
or
or
Bow - 'ry bum,
work - ing Joe,
Yes I've come a
Though I know life's
C/D
D7-9
Gm7
long
one
way
long
down the pike.
rock - y hike.
Bb/C
C7
To Coda
Ne-ver met a
Ne-ver met a
man
man
I
I
F
Fmaj7
did - n't like.
F7
Bb
C
Ne - ver shook a

F
B♭
C/E
did - n't like.
mp
F
F+
Met the worst and met the best.
Try the shoes on that are his,
mf
B♭
Gm
Some that put me to the test.
Feel what makes him what he is.
Gm/C
C7
Al - most made me change my mind.
What it's like in - side his skin,
F
Em7
A7
Yet some - how I al - ways find
Liv - in' in the skin he's in.

C/D
D7-9
f
If you don't ex - pect too much,
Just like me, a lump of sod.
Gm7
There's a cer - tain hu - man touch
There but for the grace of God,
B♭/C
1. C7
Ho - mo - sa - pi - ens has got
That is the phi -
dim.
F
B♭ Am7 Gm7
Oth - er an - i - mals have not.
2. C7
F
B♭ C
D.S. al Coda
dim. lo - so - phy Of this part time Cher - o - kee. Pres - i - dent and
mf

Coda
F
Db
did - n't like.
High - toned gent,
mp
Bow - ry bum,
Prince of Wales,
cresc.
Work - ing Joe,
Pat and Mike,
mf
Cher - o - kee, Phi - lo - so - phy.
dim.

Additional Lyrics

President and King or Pat and Mike,
Folks can laugh but
I can't give up hope.
Spun my rope a long way down the pike,
Never met a man
I didn't like.

Over The Rainbow

Words by E Y Harburg
Music by Harold Arlen

Em
C7
F
C/E
C7
o - ver the rain - bow
skies
are
blue,
F
Fm
C/G
A7(♭9)
D7
G7
and
the
dreams that you dare to
dream real - ly do come
C6
C
F/C
G7/C
true.
Some
mp
day I'll wish up - on a star and
wake up where the clouds are far be -
C6
G7
C
hind
me,
where
trou - bles melt like lem - on drops, a -
mf
Edim
Em7
E♭dim
Dm7
G7(♯5)
cresc.
way a - bove the chim - ney tops that's
where
you'll
find
me.

C Am Em C7 F C/E C7
Some - where o - ver the rain - bow blue - birds fly,
F Fm C/G A7(♭9) D7 G7
birds fly o - ver the rain - bow, why then, oh why can't
1. 2.
C6 G7 C6 C
I? I?
G7/C C6 G7
If
C Dm7 G7 C
hap-py lit - tle blue-birds fly be - yond the rain-bow, why oh why can't I?
f
mf
p
mp
rit.
pp

Singin' In The Rain

Words by Arthur Freed
Music by Nacio Herb Brown

D7
Am7
D7
laugh - ing at clouds so dark up a -
bove, the sun's in my heart and I'm
G
Am7
D
G
read - y for love. Let the storm - y clouds
mp
chase ev - 'ry - one from the place, come on with the
mf

Ddim
D7
Am7
rain, I've a smile on my face. I'll
D7
walk down the lane with a hap - py re -
Am7
D7
frain, and sing - in', just sing - in' in the
G
Em
1.Am7
C/D
G
Em
rain.
mp
cresc.
Am7
C/D
2.Am7
D7
8va
I'm
mp
p

Raindrops Keep Fallin' On My Head

Words by Hal David
Music by Burt Bacharach

Gm7
rain - drops are fall - in' on my head. They keep fall - in',
rain - drops are fall - in' on my head. They keep fall - in'!
Bb/C
C7
F
Fmaj7
B7
so I just
But there's one thing I know, the
mf
Bb
C
blues they send to meet me won't de - feat
Am7
me. It won't be long till

D7
Gm7
hap - pi - ness steps up to greet me.
B♭/C
C
B♭/C
C
F
Fmaj7
Rain - drops keep fall - in' on my head, but
mp
F7
B♭
that does - n't mean my eyes will soon be turn - in'

Am7
D7
Am7
D7
red. Cry - in's not for me 'cause
Gm7
I'm nev - er gon - na stop the rain by com - plain - in'.
B♭/C
C7
F
Am7
Be - cause I'm free,
Gm7
B♭/C
F
noth - in's wor - ry - in' me.
rit.
p

Send In The Clowns

Words and Music by Stephen Sondheim

G
D7sus4
G
bliss? Don't you ap - prove? One who keeps
Gmaj7
Cmaj7
C6
tear - ing a - round, one who can't move. Where are the
D/G
Am/D
G
clowns? Send in the clowns. Just when I'd
Bm7
F♯m7
Bm7
G
F♯m7
stopped op - en - ing doors, fin - al - ly
mf
Bm
Bm7
Gmaj7
Em
B7
know-ing the one that I want - ed was yours. Mak - ing my
f

G6/D
A/C♮
C6
B7sus4
Am7-5
en - trance a - gain with my u - su - al
flair,
sure of my
mf
Bm
Am7/D
D/G
C/E
lines,
no one is
there.
D/G
C/E
G
D7sus4
Don't you love
farce?
rich?
My fault, I
Is - n't it
mf
G
Gmaj7
fear.
queer,
I thought that
los - ing my
you'd want what I want.
tim - ing this late
Sor - ry, my
in my ca -

Cmaj7
C6
D/G
C/E
dear. But where are the clowns? Quick, send in the
reer? And where are the clowns? There ought to be
1. D/G
D7
G
D7sus4
clowns. Don't both-er, they're here.
G
D7sus4
2. D/G
D7
Is-n't it
clowns. Well, may-be next
G
D7sus4
G
year.
pp
p
dim.
rit.

Summertime

Music and Lyrics by George Gershwin, Du Bose Heyward,
Dorothy Heyward and Ira Gershwin

Am6
E7
dad - dy's rich,
and your ma is good -
look - in',
Am
D7
So
hush, lit - tle ba - by,
don't you
cry.
C
D
Dm7/G
8va
loco
One of these

Am6 E7 Am6 E7 Am E7
morn - in's you gon-na rise up sing - in',
Am E Am6 Dm
Then you'll spread your wings
Dm7 D♯dim E B7
and you'll take the sky.
E7 E7(♭5) Am6 E7
But till that morn - in'

Am6
E7
there's a noth - in' can
harm you
Am
D7
C
Am
D
Dm7/G
With Dad - dy and Mam - my stand - in'
by.
F/G
F9
mp
Bbmaj7
pp
rit.

Tomorrow

Words by Martin Charnin
Music by Charles Strouse

Fm
Fm/E♭
D♭
E♭
A♭
A♭maj7
day that's gray and lone - ly, I just stick out my chin and grin and
C7sus4
C7
F
Fmaj7
say:
Oh! The sun-'ll come out to-mor-row,
B♭maj7
Am7
Dm
Dm/C
G♭maj7
C7sus4
C7
{ So you / Oh! I } got to hang on 'til to - mor - row come what may! To -
1.F
Fmaj7
F7
B♭
B♭m
F/C
C7
mor - row, to - mor - ow, I love ya, to - mor - row, you're on - ly a day a -

F Fmaj7 B♭ C7
way! The
dim.
2.F Fmaj7
mor - row, to - mor - row, I
f
F7 B♭ B♭m F/C C7 F C7sus4 C7
love ya to - mor - row, you're al - ways a day a - way! To -
cresc.
F Fmaj7 F7 B♭ B♭m F/C
mor - row, to - - row, I love ya to - mor - row, you're on - ly a
C7sus4 C7 F Fmaj7 B♭/F B♭m F
day a - way!
ff
rit.
mf